Eugénie R. Rocherolle

Souvenirs du Château

About the Composer

Eugénie Ricau Rocherolle becomes a friend to many pianists through her piano music. Her warm, creative musical style reflects her vibrant personality.

Mrs. Rocherolle grew up in one of this country's prominent French areas–New Orleans. She spent her college junior year in Paris, where she had a class with Nadia Boulanger.

On the return boat trip from Paris, Eugénie met her future husband, Didier, whom she married a few years later. In their rural Connecticut home they have raised their daughter and three sons, and are now enjoying grandchildren! Over the years the family has spent many memorable vacations at the Château de la Rocherolle visiting with family and friends.

Eugénie R. Rocherolle

Souvenirs du Château

In the heart of France there is a lovely medieval family castle with centuries of memories; it is called Château de la Rocherolle. In this collection I have tried to capture the old and the new in a French blend of musical tapestry.

This work is lovingly dedicated to Guy and Monique Rocherolle.

E.R.R.
Wilton, Connecticut 1991

Contents

ISBN 0-8497-6183-2

Une Matinée au Lavoir

An outdoor spring-fed shallow basin,
where the laundry used to be done—
converted in recent years to a swimming area.

Andante (♩=104)

Eugénie Rocherolle

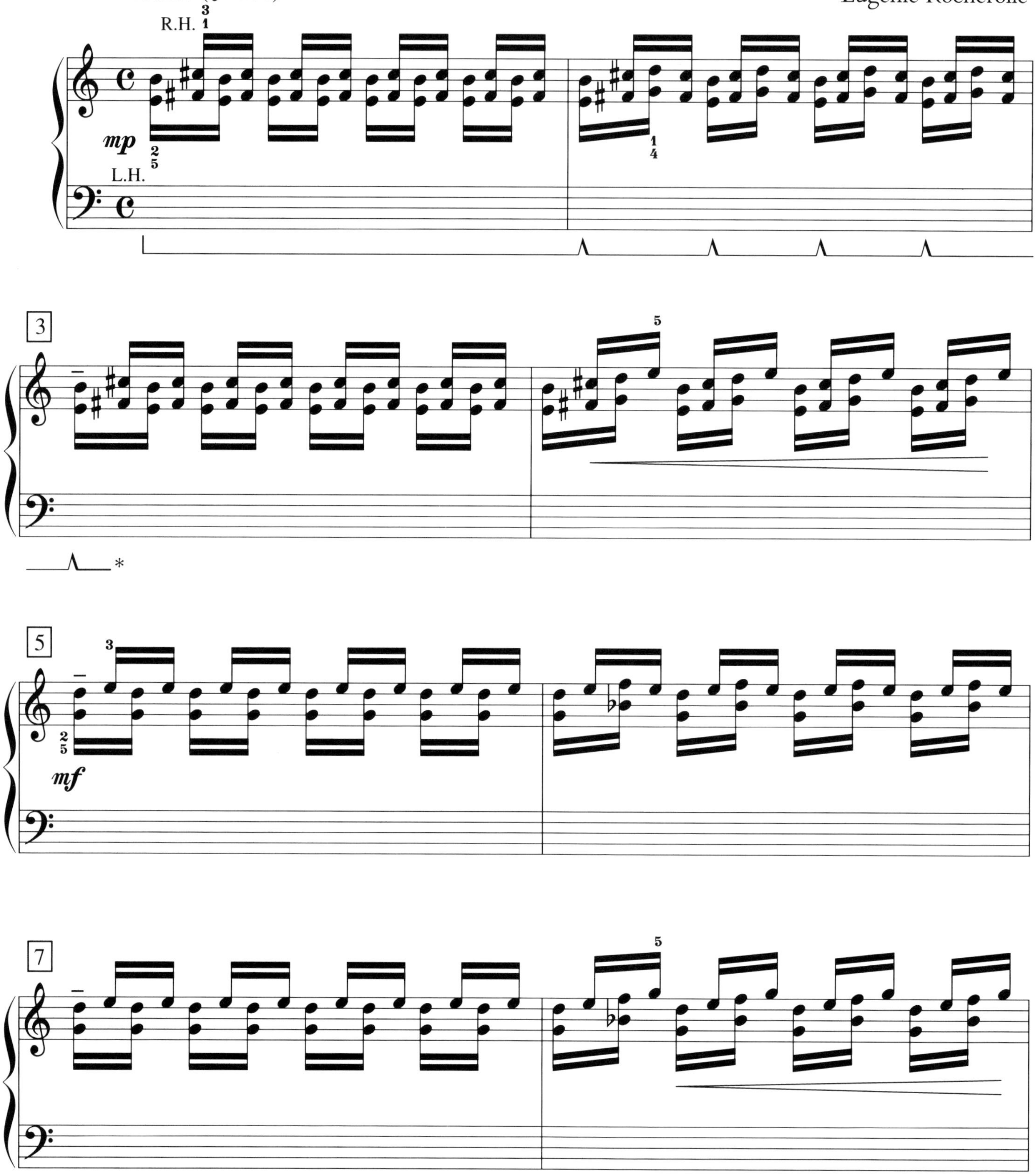

R.H. 3 1

mp

2 5

L.H.

1 4

3

5

*

*Repeat this two-measure pedal pattern except where otherwise indicated.

9
2
2
5
f
mf

11
mp

13
2
4
mf

15

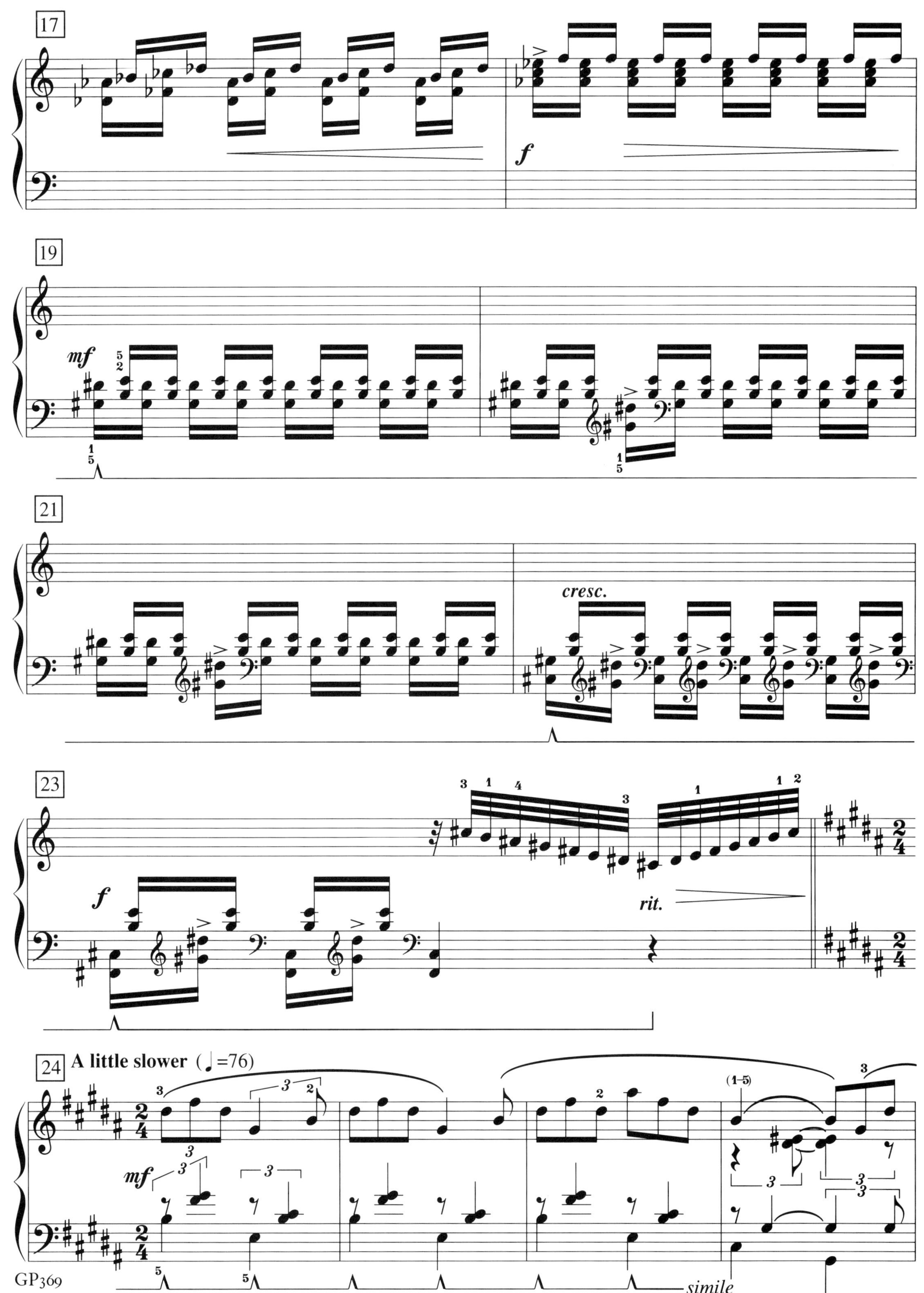

A little slower (♩=76)
mf
f
cresc.
rit.
simile

28
32
36
rit.
mp
39
A little faster (♩=92)
41

43
mf
45
47
subito p
molto cresc.
49
e accelerando
poco rit.
A little slower (♩=76)
subito mp
52
simile

55
58
mf
61
rit.
mp
64
(♩=69)
legato
66

68
cresc. e accel. poco a poco

70
1
1
poco rit.
simile

Tempo Primo (♩=104)
72
ff
L.H.

La Chapelle

Scene of several family weddings, including our daughter's in 1982.

Eugénie Rocherolle

15
Moderato (♩=112)
accel.
f
18
simile
rit.
a tempo
rit.
Tempo Primo (♩=66)
21
a tempo
poco rit.
mf
simile
24
mp
28
Andante (♩=80)
poco accel.
rit.
mf

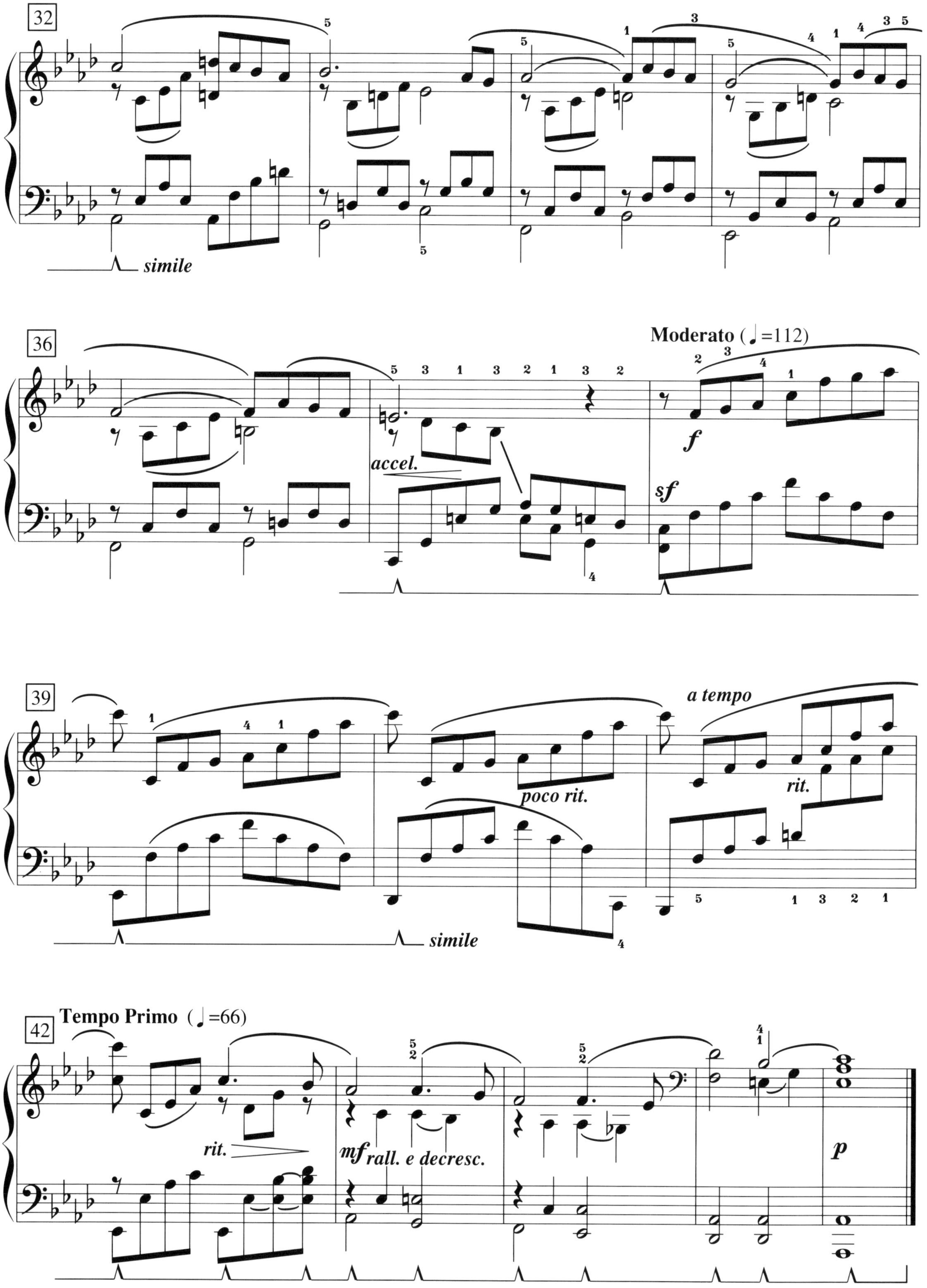

32

simile

36

Moderato (♩=112)

accel.

f

sf

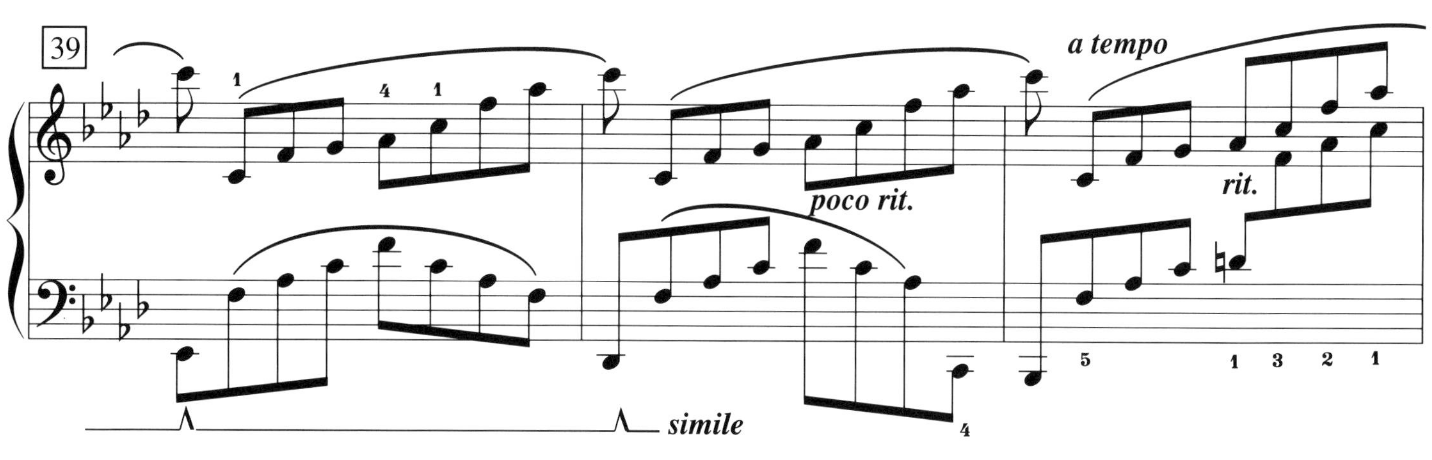

Déjeuner dans la Cour

In spring and summer, the courtyard is the social gathering place for all the family.

Eugénie Rocherolle

24
decresc.
mp
30
35
40
a tempo
poco rit.
cresc.
poco rit.
45
a tempo
f
L.H.

49
Moderato (♩=120)
poco rit.
mf
54
mp
cresc. e poco
accel.
simile
59
Tempo Primo
poco rit.
ff
63
68
Moderato (♩=120)
mf
mp
poco rit.
Tempo Primo
simile

74

a tempo

rit.

80

mf

86

92

a tempo

ritenuto

98

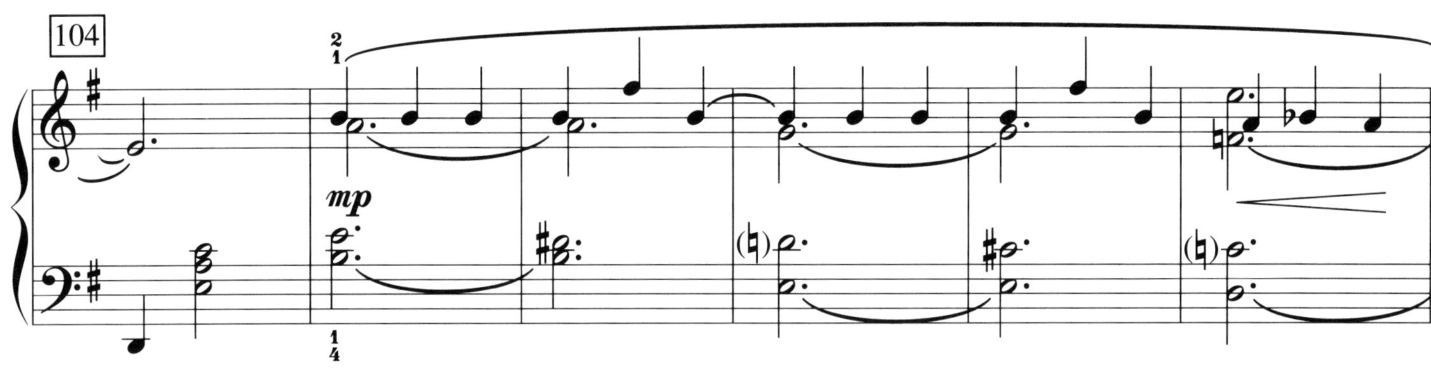
104
mp

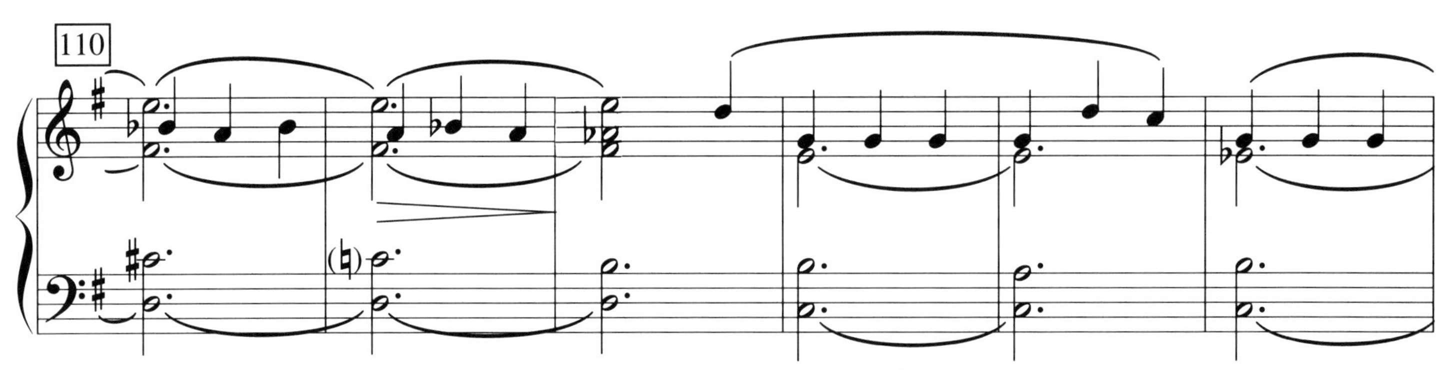
110

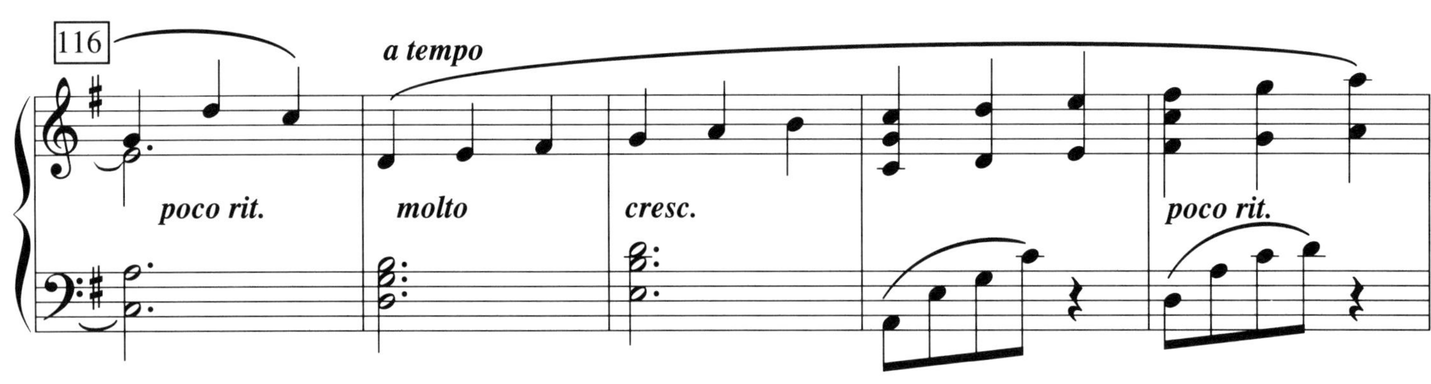
116
a tempo
poco rit.
molto
cresc.
poco rit.

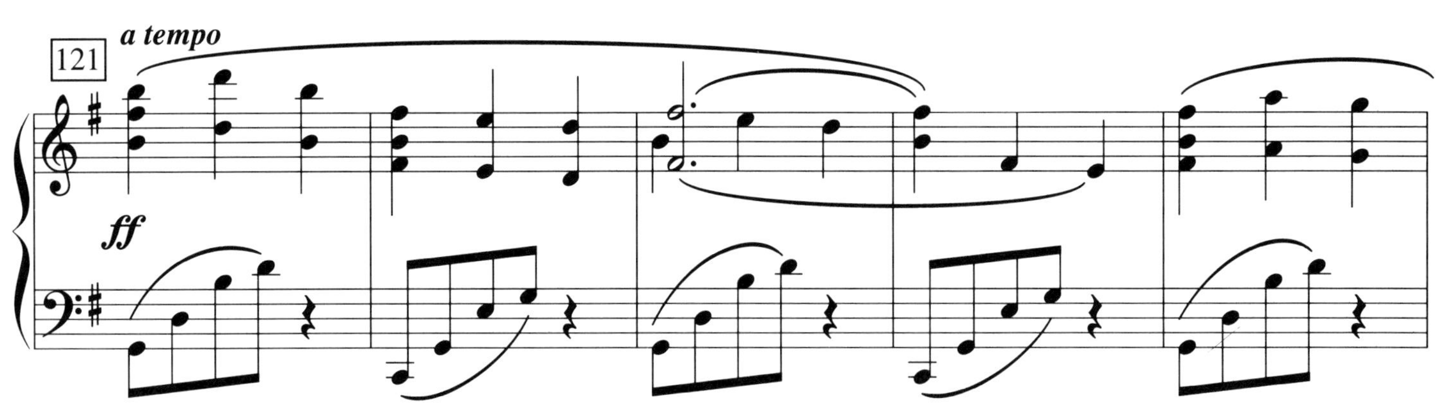
121
a tempo
ff

126
Moderato (♩=120)
poco rit.
mf

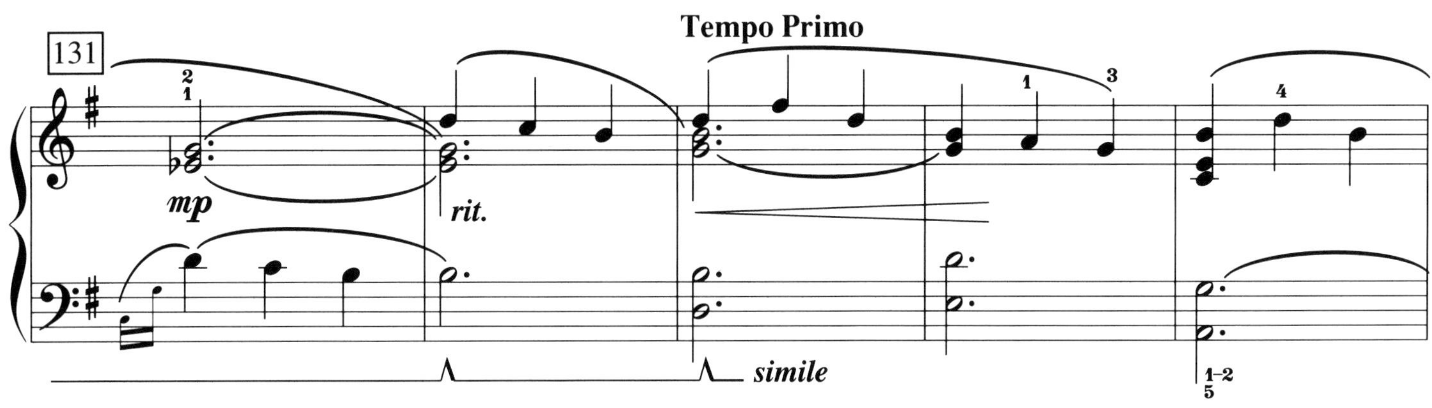
131
Tempo Primo
mp
rit.
simile

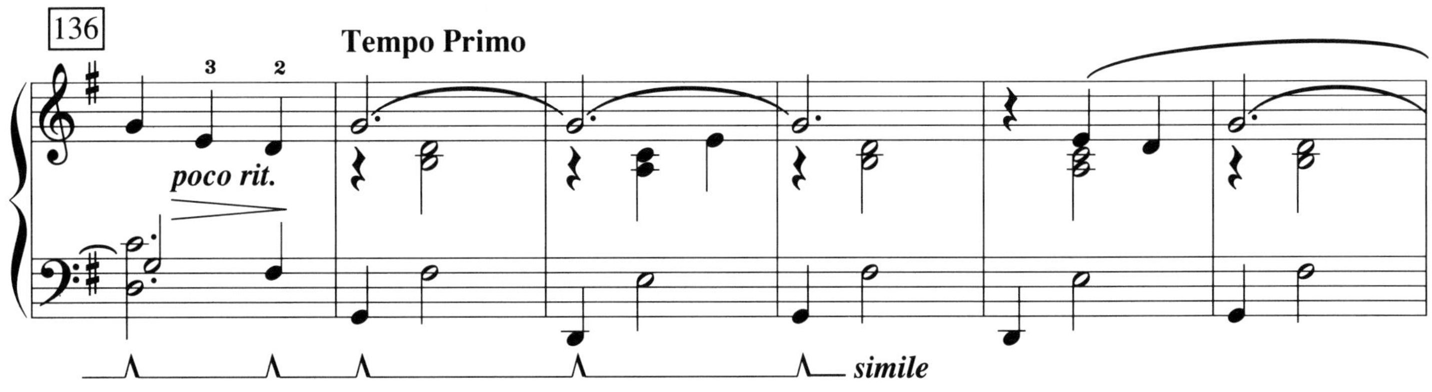
136
Tempo Primo
poco rit.
simile

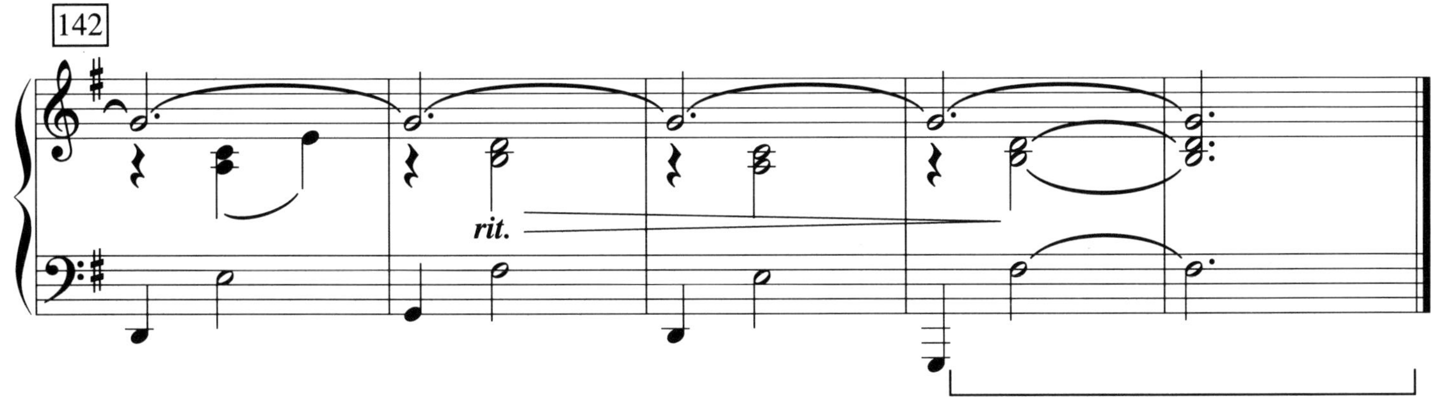
142
rit.

Le Donjon

Now used as a wine cellar or for anything that needs to be kept cool.

Eugénie Rocherolle

15
a tempo
poco rit.
mp
18
cresc.
21
f
ff
24

27
mp
cresc.
f

30

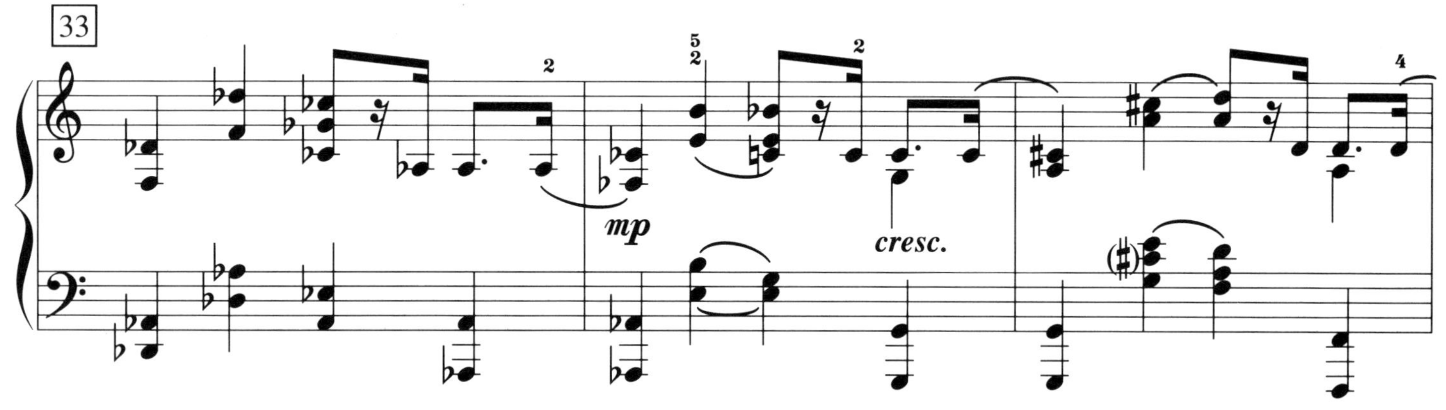
33
mp
cresc.

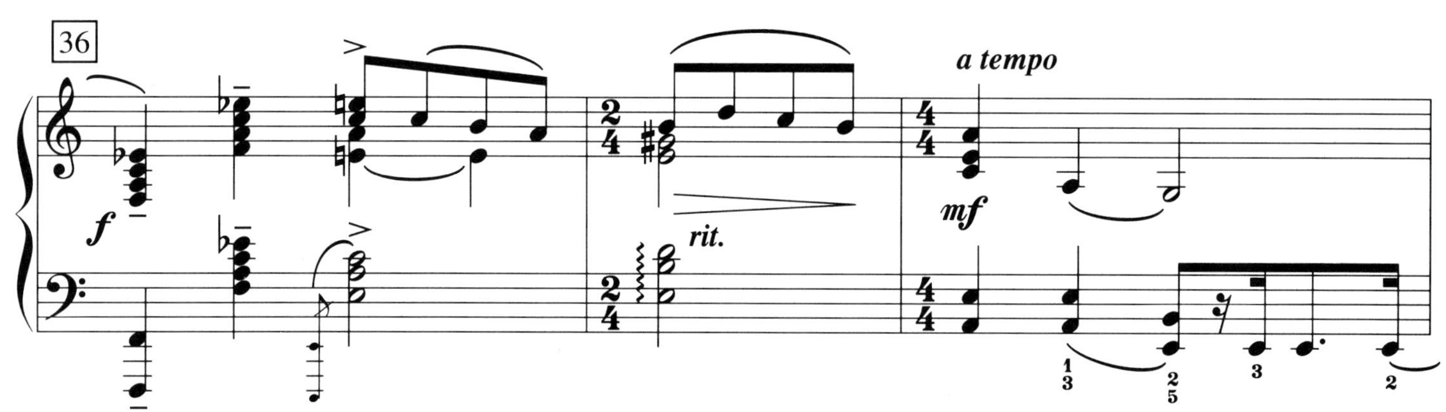
36
a tempo
f
rit.
mf

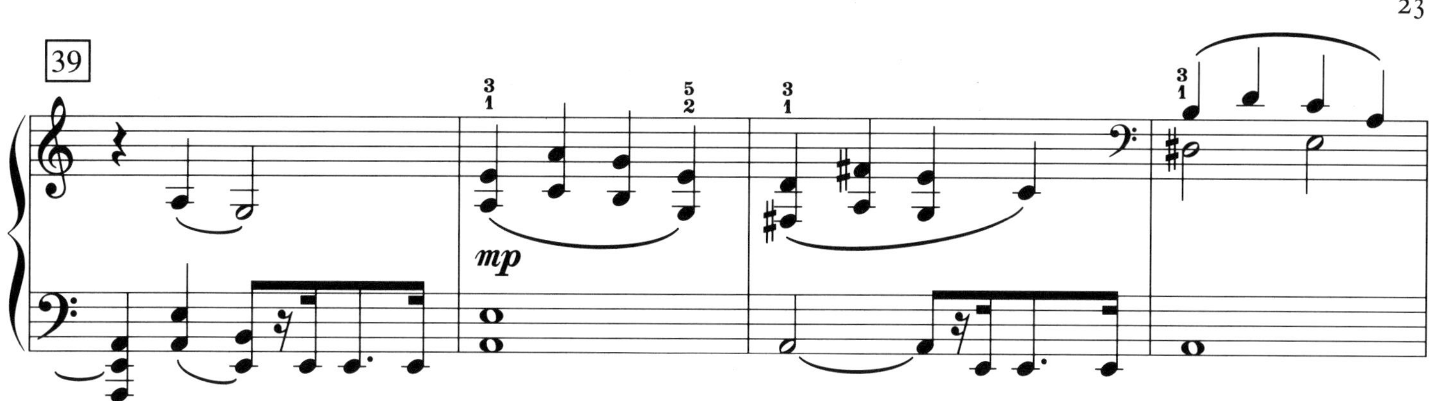
39
mp

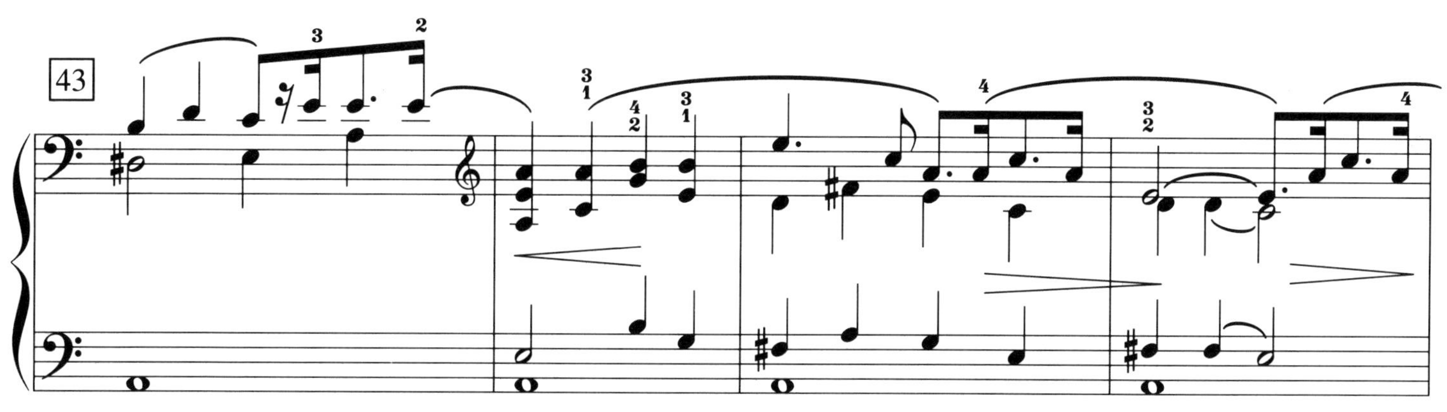
43

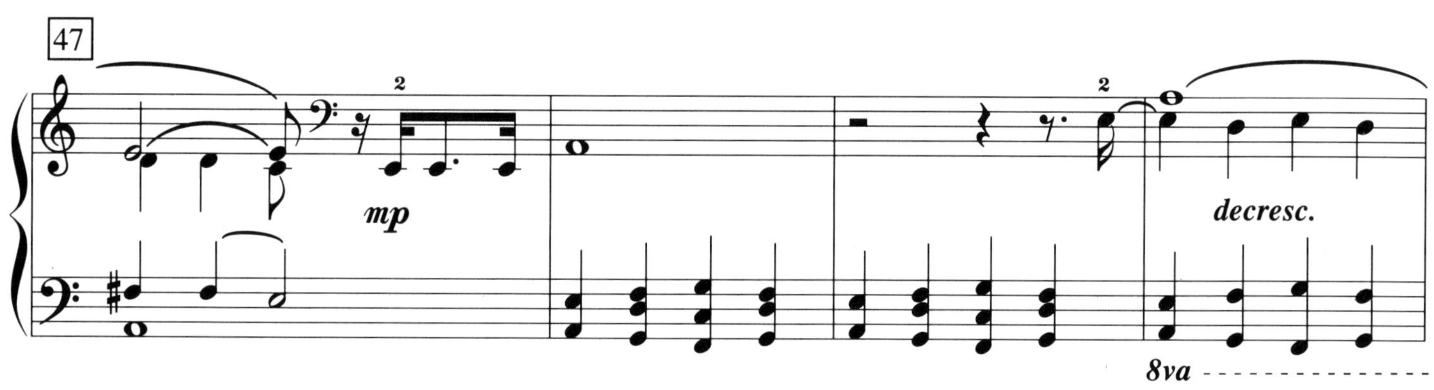
47
mp
decresc.
8va

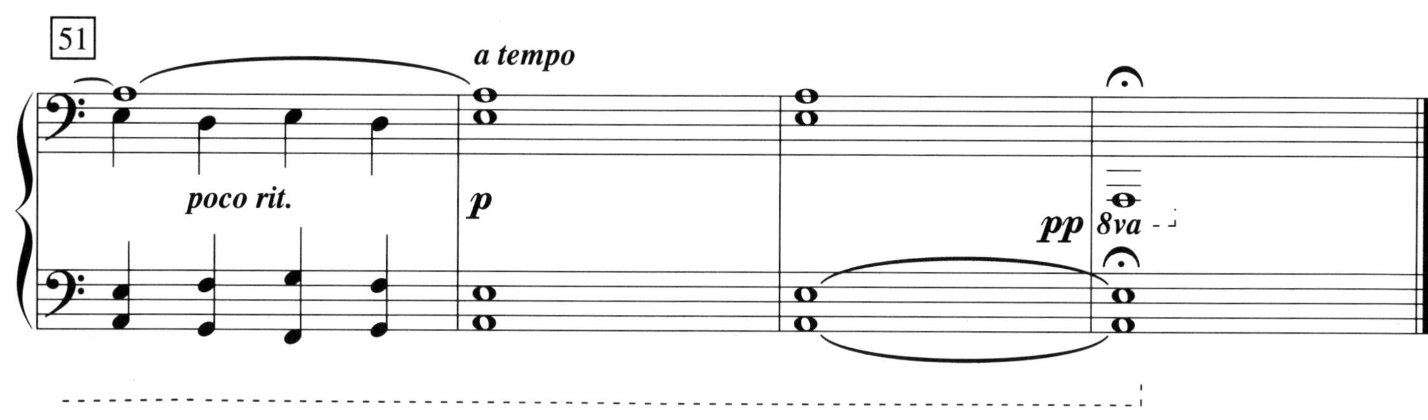
51
a tempo
poco rit.
p
pp
8va

Le Salon de Musique

Located in a round tower off the great room, the "music room" features an ornate antique Pleyel grand piano.

Eugénie Rocherolle

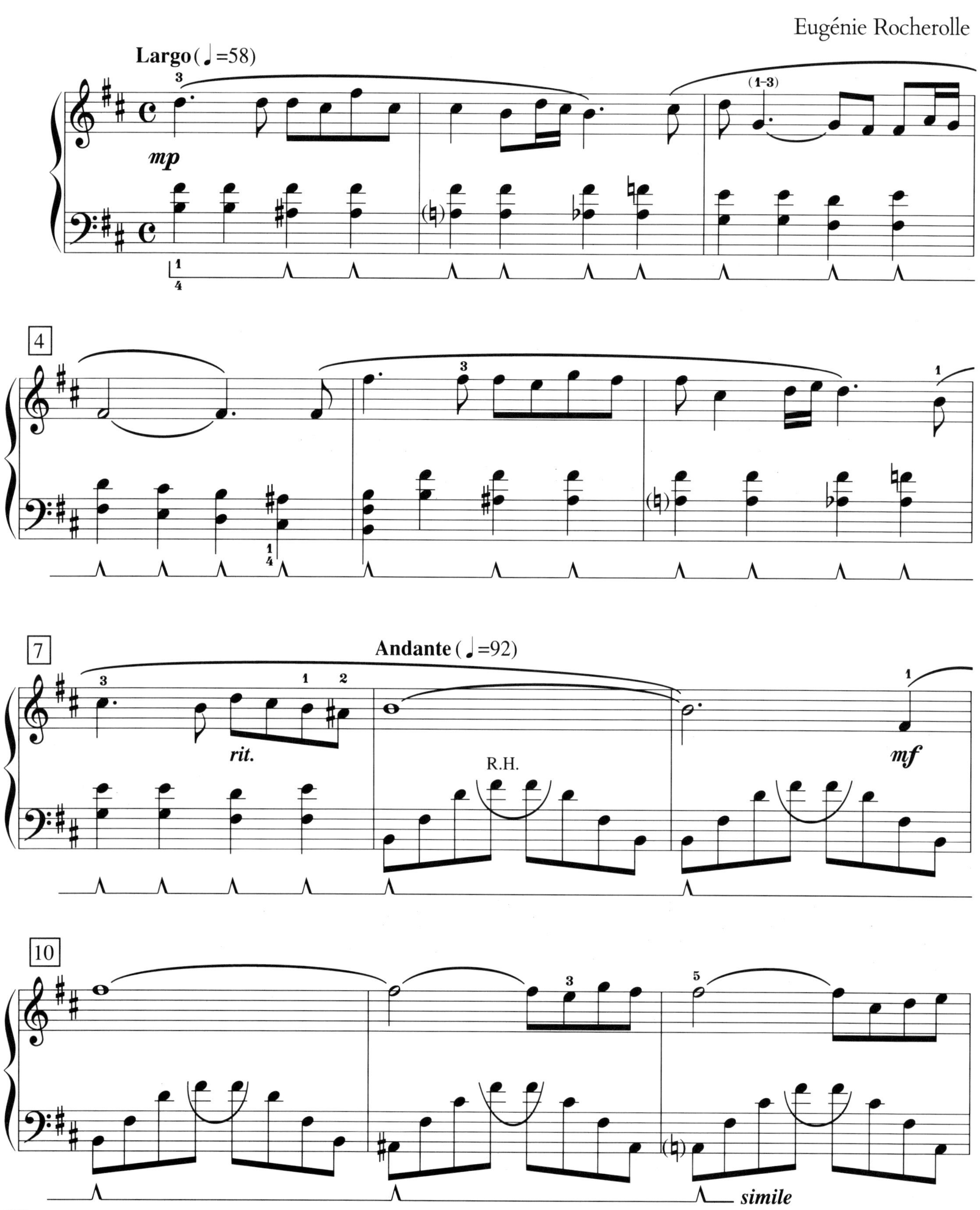

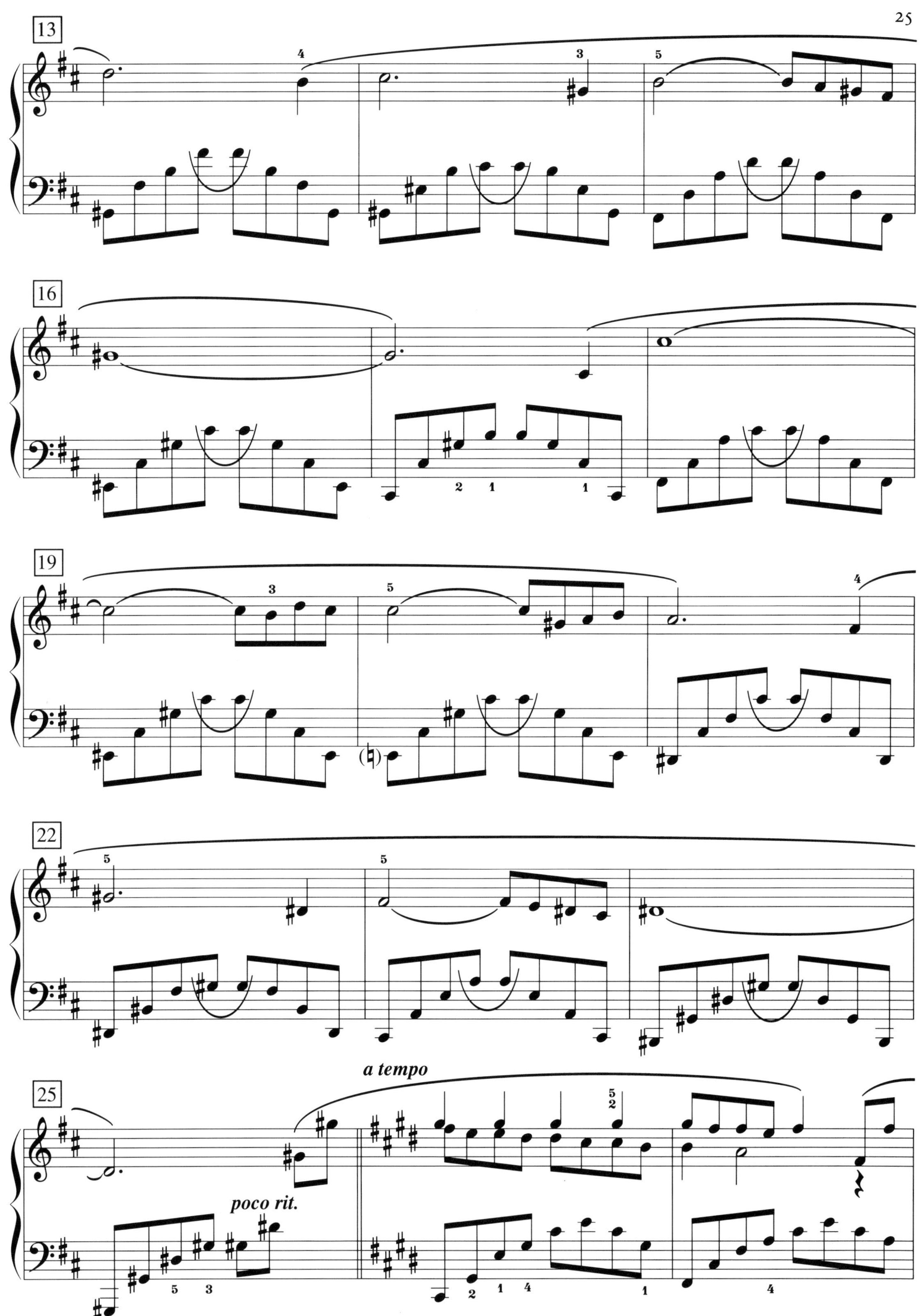
13
16
19
22
25
a tempo
poco rit.

28
31
cresc.
poco rit.
(1–5)
34
Allegro (♩=160)
mp
simile
38
cresc.
42
8va
f
8va

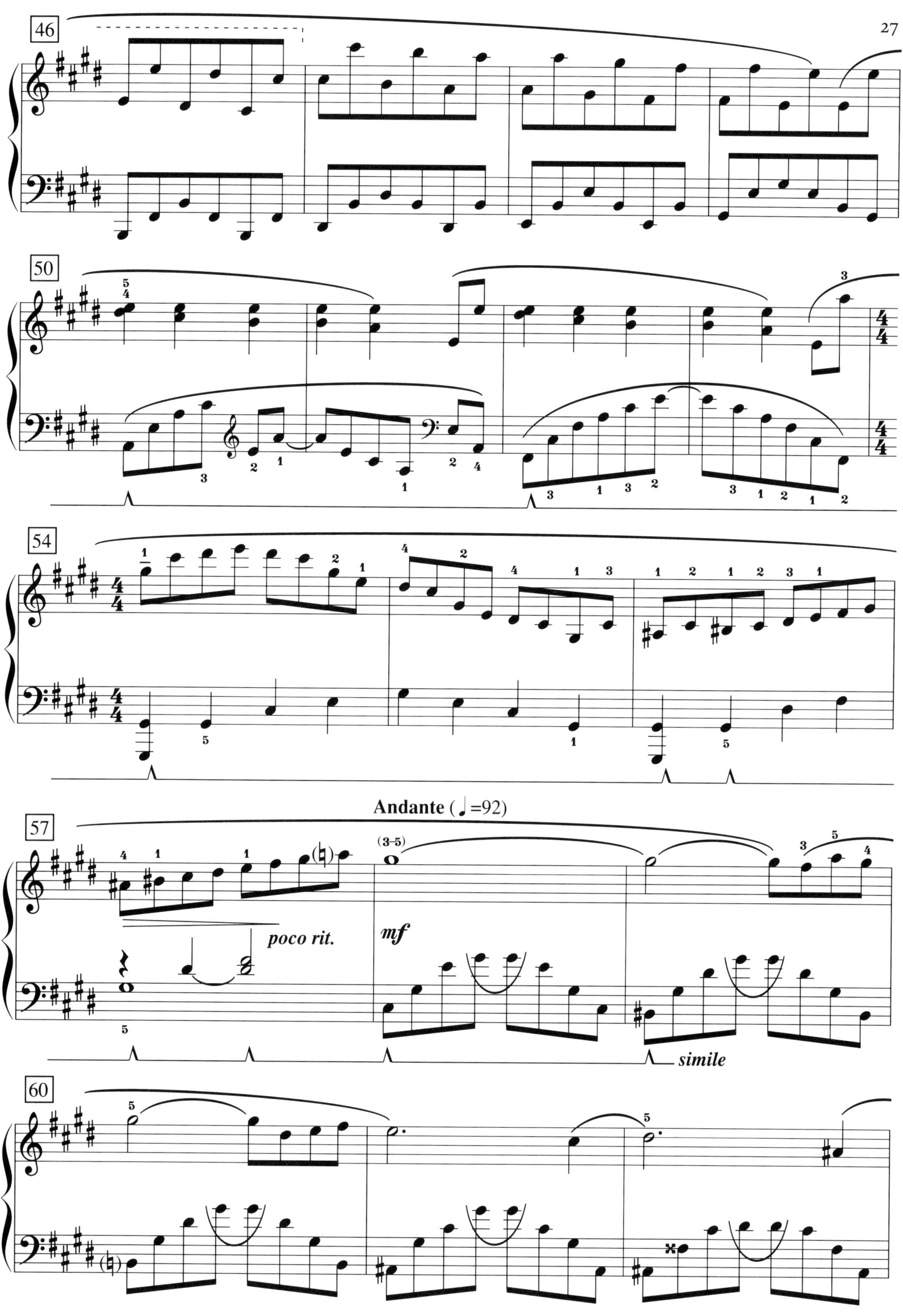
46
50
54
Andante (♩=92)
57
poco rit.
mf
simile
60

63
66
69
72

75
poco rit.
mp

78

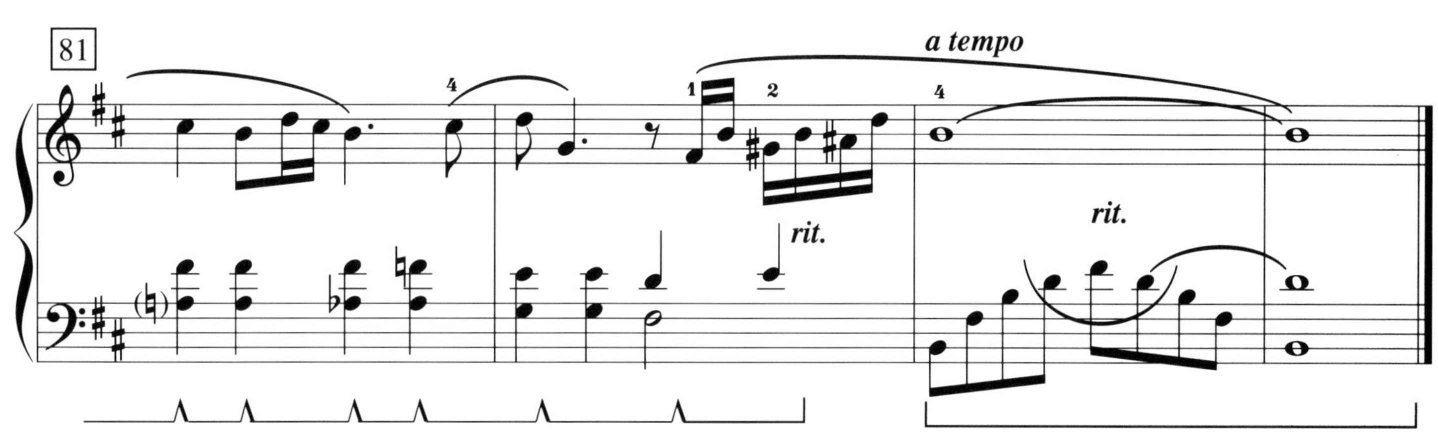
81
a tempo
rit.
rit.